7 SIMPLE STEPS to STUDYING SCRIPTURE

Teen Edition

How to Journal Your Way through the Word of God

Angella Bundz
with Molly Bundz

Dedication

You may have never read a book dedicated to you...the reader...but this one is. We are dedicating this book to the teens who want to find the one true God. The teens who want to fall in love with the Lord and His word while living their lives for Him. Wherever you are in your walk of faith, God is right there with you.

We are too.

1 Timothy 4:12 NIV
"Don't let anyone look down on you because you are young, but set an example for the believers in speech, in conduct, in love, in faith, and in purity."

www.AngellaBundz.com

Graphics on cover and pages courtesy of Freepik.com/rawpixel.com

ISBN: 978-0-578-77580-7 (print)

Printed in the United States of America.

Acknowledgements

I thank the Lord Jesus Christ for being my Savior and for allowing me to join Him in Kingdom work. I am forever grateful.

I thank my husband, Sam, and our three daughters, Katie, Grace, and Molly for all of your love and support. I'm thankful we get to do life together as a family and that God continues to use us for His glory. I love watching you all seek after Him. I love you all always.

I am grateful for my daughter, Molly, and her help working on this very book. She loves Jesus well and wanted to help teens grow closer to Him through an easier to understand way to read the Bible. Thank you for seeking after God about the themes and verses to include in this book. I am proud of you. Dad and I love you always.

Thank you to Amanda Foust with Homegrown Writing Collective for her amazing editing work.

Thank you to Denae Hively with The Hively Co. for her wonderful website design and behind-the-scenes guidance.

Thank you to Lorie DeWorken with Mind the Margins for her beautiful cover and inside design of this book.

You all make things beautiful for me, and I am grateful that God led me to you.

—Angella

I am so thankful to God for this opportunity to help write a book with my mom.

Thank you Jesus for your unending grace and love that surpasses all understanding; I am so grateful.

Thank you to my family for helping me grow in my faith as I have grown older.

—Molly

A Note from Molly

Hi friend!

I am so glad you have this journaling book in your hands. For a long time, I have been searching for a Christian book for teens to help get me into the Word. Still to this day, I have not found anything like this book right here. My mom first wrote the adult version of this book, and we were both inspired to create something for people my age, too. As a teenager in this culture, we are constantly trying to fight standards, and it's a difficult daily battle. The Bible has helped me to understand that I no longer need to measure up to standards or others' expectations of me, because I am who God says I am. This gives me comfort and satisfaction that God calls us to be different and live a unique lifestyle according to His Word.

God's Word is a powerful tool that you can use in your daily life. This journaling book will help you get into the Word of God, while also helping you see the Bible in a whole new way. When you are able to understand the Bible better, you can learn how much He loves you and the promises He has for your life. I cannot wait to see how God uses this book for the glory of His Kingdom!

A Note from Angella

I am so glad that you are here! God loves you! God promises that He has good plans for you! In this book, there are 7 steps that you will repeat each time that you read your Bible. God put these on my heart to share with others to help them easily understand His Word and to draw closer to Him! These 7 steps will help you see what God is saying to you, personally!

You may be asking yourself, "What supplies do I need to journal through the Bible?" Well, I like to keep things simple. You just need something to write with and a tablet, a Bible or Bible app and this book. If you want to get more creative you can get a list of tools at my website Angellabundz.com/tools

I am so proud of my daughter, Molly, who wanted to help me write a version of my book for teens. She chose the 12 topics for the book. She felt that the topics are very relevant and needed by teens and young people today. It is her desire also, to see many others come to know the love and salvation of Jesus Christ.

I cannot wait to see all that God will do through you as you grow closer to Him.

The 7 steps will help you to seek after God and easily learn what He is saying to you, personally.

Understanding the 7 Steps

1. Scripture

After finding which topic you would like to study, you will start by looking up the verse that is listed on the top of the page. You can use whatever Bible translation that you prefer. Keep in mind that some Bible translations are more literal and others are more of a paraphrase. You can also use a Bible app on your phone. Personally, I like to hold the Word on paper in my hands.

Next, you will write down the verse in your own handwriting. There are benefits to actually writing Scripture. It helps you to slow down, lean in, and really read the words. It also helps you to interact with His words in the Bible. You can see the details that you may have missed if you were reading too quickly.

Looking up the Scripture ourselves helps us become more familiar with our Bible. There truly is power in the Word when it is written on paper. Don't worry...you don't need to be an artist or have beautiful handwriting to do this step. Simply write the verse to get it into your head and heart. If you do want to bring more artistry to the process, feel free to unleash your creativity! (I even have some blank pages in the book for this purpose).

2. Soak It In

Next, you will read a verse or verses a few times—even aloud. The repetitive reading of the same verse will help you to soak in the message God has for you.

TIP: You may want to read different versions of the Bible to see if they make the verse easier to understand.

3. Search Meanings

This step is a favorite of many who use the 7-step method. You will write down definitions of new words where you may not understand the meaning when you are reading the designated Bible verse. I recommend that even looking up a common word like "joy" will bring a new understanding to the Scripture. When you understand the Word of God better, the verses really come alive in a way that's personal to you.

4. Saying to Me

Just like this step states, you will write down what you feel God is saying to you through the listed Bible verse. This will be a little different to everyone, because God wants a personal relationship with each of us. When we learn about God's truths and His love for us, it is very powerful to write down what God reveals. You may not fully understand it now, but you may look back on it later and see God's hand moving! This is so powerful because it is not just a broad application; you are asking God to show you what He has for you, personally.

5. Set Your Mind

We are called in Colossians 3:2 to set our minds on things above, not on earthly things. So this is the step where you decide to set your mind and thoughts on the truths that you have learned. Although we cannot escape the stress and troubles of this world, we can choose to focus above on the truth and love of Jesus Christ. We can choose to believe the truths of God, not the lies and discouragements of the enemy. In this section, review what you have learned from the Bible verse(s) and write down a sentence or two that you choose to remember and carry with you.

6. Share

This is the step where you think about ways you can share the truths you have learned with others. You can do this through a number of ways such as sharing a social media post, sending a text to a friend, mailing a note to a friend, or by sharing what you have learned to the ones closest to you. When we share God's truths with others, it provides hope and encouragement to the ones around us. Let's spread some hope and joy today!

7. Say It In A Prayer

In this last step, you will write a simple prayer to God. He loves spending time with you. Remember, prayer is just talking and listening to God. It helps us form a closer relationship with Him. There are many Bible verses with promises that talk about prayer. These prayers in this step are generally related to the Bible topic you are studying. You will then have a record of prayers that you can go back and read again and again. It is an honor to be able to talk to God at any time about anything.

Those are the 7 steps that you will repeat each and every day. Along the way, you will gain a new understanding of God's Word that brings meaning and life to you. Draw near to Him and develop a habit of seeking His will for your life!

On the next page you'll see a brief layout of the 7 steps to refer back to if you feel stuck along the way.

Remember, there is no perfection here. Jesus Christ is the only perfect one who ever lived. Our goal here is to fall in love with God and His Word. If you feel stuck or unsure, you can literally say to God, "Lord, I am not understanding this, please help me." We can ask the Holy Spirit to reveal His truths. He is here for you, and I am too.

We can't wait for you to get started!

Angella and Molly

7 SIMPLE STEPS to STUDYING SCRIPTURE

1. SCRIPTURE—Write down the verse in your own handwriting.

2. SOAK IT IN—Meditate on the Word by reading the verse at least three times and even saying it out loud.

3. SEARCH MEANINGS—Write down the word(s) that you don't understand, or want to learn about, and search their meanings.

4. SAYING TO ME—Write down what you feel God is showing you through that verse.

5. SET YOUR MIND—Write down what you choose to carry with you and keep in your thoughts.

6. SHARE—Plan how you will share what you've learned.

7. SAY IT IN A PRAYER—Pray a simple prayer to God.

Sample Journal Entry

Date: 9/18/20

Psalm 36:7

1 Scripture "The Lord will fight for you, you only need to be still."

2 Soak It In I reread 3 times, you may reread however many times you want!

3 Search Meanings

Fight – to contend in battle or physical combat; to put forth a determined effort

need – require (something) because it is essential or very important

Still – deep silence and calm; stillness; not moving or making a sound

x

4 **Saying To Me** I try to fight my own battles for so long but Lord, through this verse, you are showing me that I need to place my battles in your hands! The Lord has already won every single battle we will ever face, so I need to trust God and His Strength.

5 **Set Your Mind** I choose to remember that You, Lord fight all of My battles! You have won every single battle you have faced in the past, present, and future.

6 **Share** I shared this verse in a letter I wrote a friend today.

7 **Say It In a Prayer** Dear Lord,
Thank You for fighting all of my battles, even when I don't realize it. You are a God full of Strength and courage. Thank you for always being there for me every step of the way. Please help me realize that YOU will always go before me to fight My battles.
In Jesus' name, Amen.

Our prayer for you...

God wants you to know Him and His love for you! His Word was given to us with love, grace, and truth.

> Dear God, I pray for each teen/young person who uses this journal. Being a teen in this day and age is not easy. But we know from your Word, the Bible, you are greater than anything in this world. I ask that you would show up in a mighty way in their life. I ask that you would give them understanding and clarity as they seek after you and your Word. I ask you, Lord, to help them understand and experience how wide, long, high, and deep your love is for them.
>
> Please help them to know that you are our only real hope. Because hope is not found in popularity, status, appearance, attention, followers, or friends. You promise us in the Bible that you will never leave us or forsake us; please help these teens to remember this truth always. In our society that is constantly moving and changing, I ask that your voice of wisdom and love be the focus of their life.
>
> Lord, You have often called teens to do your mighty work. We see examples of this in Mary, David, and Esther from the Bible. I ask that this reader would fall in love with you and your Word for the remainder of their days. I pray that this teen will live their life for You and have You at the center of their hearts.
>
> In Jesus name,
> Amen

We cannot wait to hear all that God will do in and through you.

Please keep in touch and share your God stories.

You can reach Molly at molly.bundz@gmail.com IG: molly.bundz FB: Molly Bundz

You can reach Angella at angellabundz.com angellabundz@gmail.com IG: angella.bundz FB: Angella Bundz

Table of Contents

Who God Says You Are

God's Love for You

A Season of Waiting

A Call to Be Different

Battling Comparison

Scared and Afraid

Be Content and Thankful

Find Strength Through God

Forgiven and Healed

Beautifully and Wonderfully Made

You Have a Purpose

Trust in the Lord

Who God Says You Are

Who God Says You Are

You are wonderfully made.

Date:

Psalm 139:13-14

1 Scripture

2 Soak It In

3 Search Meanings

4 Saying To Me

5 Set Your Mind

6 Share

7 Say It In a Prayer

Who God Says You Are

You have been rejected, but God says you're His.

Date:

Isaiah 43:1

1 Scripture

2 Soak It In

3 Search Meanings

4 Saying To Me

5 Set Your Mind

6 Share

7 Say It In a Prayer

Who God Says You Are

You are precious.

Date: ______________________

Isaiah 43:4

1 Scripture

2 Soak It In

3 Search Meanings

4 Saying To Me

5 Set Your Mind

6 Share

7 Say It In a Prayer

Who God Says You Are

You are loved.

Date:

Jeremiah 31:3

1 Scripture

2 Soak It In

3 Search Meanings

4 Saying To Me

5 Set Your Mind

6 Share

7 Say It In a Prayer

Who God Says You Are

You have failed, but you are victorious through Jesus Christ.

Date:

I Corinthians 15:57

1 Scripture

2 Soak It In

3 Search Meanings

4 Saying To Me

5 Set Your Mind

6 Share

7 Say It In a Prayer

Who God Says You Are

You have been set free.

Date:

Ephesians 1:7

1 Scripture

2 Soak It In

3 Search Meanings

4 Saying To Me

5 Set Your Mind

6 Share

7 Say It In a Prayer

GOD'S LOVE FOR YOU

God's Love for You

Date:

Psalm 36:7

1 Scripture

2 Soak It In

3 Search Meanings

4 Saying To Me

5 Set Your Mind

6 Share

7 Say It In a Prayer

God's Love for You

Date: ____________________

Psalm 86:15

1 Scripture

2 Soak It In

3 Search Meanings

4 Saying To Me

5 Set Your Mind

6 Share

7 Say It In a Prayer

God's Love for You

Date:

Isaiah 54:10

1 Scripture

2 Soak It In

3 Search Meanings

4 Saying To Me

5 Set Your Mind

6 Share

7 Say It In a Prayer

God's Love for You

Date:

Zephaniah 3:17

1 Scripture

2 Soak It In

3 Search Meanings

4 Saying To Me

5 Set Your Mind

6 Share

7 Say It In a Prayer

God's Love for You

Date:

John 3:16

1 Scripture

2 Soak It In

3 Search Meanings

4 Saying To Me

5 Set Your Mind

6 Share

7 Say It In a Prayer

God's Love for You

Date:

Romans 8:38-39

1 Scripture

2 Soak It In

3 Search Meanings

4 Saying To Me

5 Set Your Mind

6 Share

7 Say It In a Prayer

God's Love for You

Date:

Ephesians 2:4-5

1 Scripture

2 Soak It In

3 Search Meanings

4 Saying To Me

5 Set Your Mind

6 Share

7 Say It In a Prayer

A SEASON OF WAITING

A Season of Waiting

Date: ____________________

Psalm 27:14

1 Scripture

2 Soak It In

3 Search Meanings

4 Saying To Me

5 Set Your Mind

6 Share

7 Say It In a Prayer

A Season of Waiting

Date:

Psalm 31:14-15

1 Scripture

2 Soak It In

3 Search Meanings

4 Saying To Me

5 Set Your Mind

6 Share

7 Say It In a Prayer

A Season of Waiting

Date:

Psalm 62:8

1 Scripture

2 Soak It In

3 Search Meanings

4 Saying To Me

5 Set Your Mind

6 Share

7 Say It In a Prayer

A Season of Waiting

Date: ______

Proverbs 3:5-7

1 Scripture

2 Soak It In

3 Search Meanings

4 Saying To Me

5 Set Your Mind

6 Share

7 Say It In a Prayer

A Season of Waiting

Date:

Isaiah 40:31

1 Scripture

2 Soak It In

3 Search Meanings

4 Saying To Me

5 Set Your Mind

6 Share

7 Say It In a Prayer

A CALL TO BE DIFFERENT

A Call to Be Different

Date:

Psalm 119:9

1 Scripture

2 Soak It In

3 Search Meanings

4 Saying To Me

5 Set Your Mind

6 Share

7 Say It In a Prayer

A Call to Be Different

Date:

Luke 6:35

1 Scripture

2 Soak It In

3 Search Meanings

4 Saying To Me

5 Set Your Mind

6 Share

7 Say It In a Prayer

A Call to Be Different

Date:

Romans 12:2

1 Scripture

2 Soak It In

3 Search Meanings

4 Saying To Me

5 Set Your Mind

6 Share

7 Say It In a Prayer

A Call to Be Different

Date:

Galatians 1:10

1 Scripture

2 Soak It In

3 Search Meanings

4 Saying To Me

5 Set Your Mind

6 Share

7 Say It In a Prayer

A Call to Be Different

Date:

Galatians 6:9

1 Scripture

2 Soak It In

3 Search Meanings

4 Saying To Me

5 Set Your Mind

6 Share

7 Say It In a Prayer

A Call to Be Different

Date:

Colossians 3:12

1 Scripture

2 Soak It In

3 Search Meanings

4 Saying To Me

5 Set Your Mind

6 Share

7 Say It In a Prayer

A Call to Be Different

Date:

Colossians 3:17

1 Scripture

2 Soak It In

3 Search Meanings

4 Saying To Me

5 Set Your Mind

6 Share

7 Say It In a Prayer

A Call to Be Different

Date:

I John 2:15

1 Scripture

2 Soak It In

3 Search Meanings

4 Saying To Me

5 Set Your Mind

6 Share

7 Say It In a Prayer

BATTLING COMPARISON

Battling Comparison

Date:

Romans 12:6

1 Scripture

2 Soak It In

3 Search Meanings

4 Saying To Me

5 Set Your Mind

6 Share

7 Say It In a Prayer

Battling Comparison

Date:

Galatians 1:10

1 Scripture

2 Soak It In

3 Search Meanings

4 Saying To Me

5 Set Your Mind

6 Share

7 Say It In a Prayer

Battling Comparison

Date: ____________________

Galatians 6:4

1 Scripture

2 Soak It In

3 Search Meanings

4 Saying To Me

5 Set Your Mind

6 Share

7 Say It In a Prayer

Battling Comparison

Date:

Philippians 2:3-4

1 Scripture

2 Soak It In

3 Search Meanings

4 Saying To Me

5 Set Your Mind

6 Share

7 Say It In a Prayer

Scared and Afraid

Scared and Afraid

Date: ____________________

Deuteronomy 31:6

1 Scripture

2 Soak It In

3 Search Meanings

4 Saying To Me

5 Set Your Mind

6 Share

7 Say It In a Prayer

Scared and Afraid

Date:

Joshua 1:9

1 Scripture

2 Soak It In

3 Search Meanings

4 Saying To Me

5 Set Your Mind

6 Share

7 Say It In a Prayer

Scared and Afraid

Date: ______________________

Psalm 23:4

1 Scripture

2 Soak It In

3 Search Meanings

4 Saying To Me

5 Set Your Mind

6 Share

7 Say It In a Prayer

Scared and Afraid

Date:

Psalm 27:1

1 Scripture

2 Soak It In

3 Search Meanings

4 Saying To Me

5 Set Your Mind

6 Share

7 Say It In a Prayer

Scared and Afraid

Date:

Psalm 34:4

1 Scripture

2 Soak It In

3 Search Meanings

4 Saying To Me

5 Set Your Mind

6 Share

7 Say It In a Prayer

Scared and Afraid

Date:

Psalm 94:19

1 Scripture

2 Soak It In

3 Search Meanings

4 Saying To Me

5 Set Your Mind

6 Share

7 Say It In a Prayer

Scared and Afraid

Date: ______

Isaiah 41:10

1 Scripture

2 Soak It In

3 Search Meanings

4 Saying To Me

5 Set Your Mind

6 Share

7 Say It In a Prayer

Scared and Afraid

Date:

Isaiah 43:1

1 Scripture

2 Soak It In

3 Search Meanings

4 Saying To Me

5 Set Your Mind

6 Share

7 Say It In a Prayer

Scared and Afraid

Date:

John 14:27

1 Scripture

2 Soak It In

3 Search Meanings

4 Saying To Me

5 Set Your Mind

6 Share

7 Say It In a Prayer

Scared and Afraid

Date:

Philippians 4:6-7, 13

1 Scripture

2 Soak It In

3 Search Meanings

4 Saying To Me

5 Set Your Mind

6 Share

7 Say It In a Prayer

Scared and Afraid

Date:

2 Timothy 1:7

1 Scripture

2 Soak It In

3 Search Meanings

4 Saying To Me

5 Set Your Mind

6 Share

7 Say It In a Prayer

Scared and Afraid

Date:

I Peter 5:7

1 Scripture

2 Soak It In

3 Search Meanings

4 Saying To Me

5 Set Your Mind

6 Share

7 Say It In a Prayer

BE CONTENT AND THANKFUL

Be Content and Thankful

Date:

I Chronicles 16:34

1 Scripture

2 Soak It In

3 Search Meanings

4 Saying To Me

5 Set Your Mind

6 Share

7 Say It In a Prayer

Be Content and Thankful

Date:

Psalm 9:1

1 Scripture

2 Soak It In

3 Search Meanings

4 Saying To Me

5 Set Your Mind

6 Share

7 Say It In a Prayer

Be Content and Thankful

Date:

Psalm 69:30

1 Scripture

2 Soak It In

3 Search Meanings

4 Saying To Me

5 Set Your Mind

6 Share

7 Say It In a Prayer

Be Content and Thankful

Date:

Psalm 95:2-3

1 Scripture

2 Soak It In

3 Search Meanings

4 Saying To Me

5 Set Your Mind

6 Share

7 Say It In a Prayer

Be Content and Thankful

Date:

Psalm 106:1

1 Scripture

2 Soak It In

3 Search Meanings

4 Saying To Me

5 Set Your Mind

6 Share

7 Say It In a Prayer

Be Content and Thankful

Date:

Daniel 2:23

1 Scripture

2 Soak It In

3 Search Meanings

4 Saying To Me

5 Set Your Mind

6 Share

7 Say It In a Prayer

Be Content and Thankful

Date:

Colossians 3:17

1 Scripture

2 Soak It In

3 Search Meanings

4 Saying To Me

5 Set Your Mind

6 Share

7 Say It In a Prayer

Be Content and Thankful

Date:

I Thessalonians 5:18

1 Scripture

2 Soak It In

3 Search Meanings

4 Saying To Me

5 Set Your Mind

6 Share

7 Say It In a Prayer

FIND STRENGTH THROUGH GOD

Find Strength Through God

Date:

Exodus 14:14

1 Scripture

2 Soak It In

3 Search Meanings

4 Saying To Me

5 Set Your Mind

6 Share

7 Say It In a Prayer

Find Strength Through God

Date:

Lamentations 3:22-23

1 Scripture

2 Soak It In

3 Search Meanings

4 Saying To Me

5 Set Your Mind

6 Share

7 Say It In a Prayer

Find Strength Through God

Date:

Matthew 19:26

1 Scripture

2 Soak It In

3 Search Meanings

4 Saying To Me

5 Set Your Mind

6 Share

7 Say It In a Prayer

Find Strength Through God

Date:

Luke 1:37

1 Scripture

2 Soak It In

3 Search Meanings

4 Saying To Me

5 Set Your Mind

6 Share

7 Say It In a Prayer

Find Strength Through God

Date:

Philippians 4:13

1 Scripture

2 Soak It In

3 Search Meanings

4 Saying To Me

5 Set Your Mind

6 Share

7 Say It In a Prayer

Forgiven and Healed

Forgiven and Healed

Date:

Isaiah 1:18

1 Scripture

2 Soak It In

3 Search Meanings

4 Saying To Me

5 Set Your Mind

6 Share

7 Say It In a Prayer

Forgiven and Healed

Date:

Acts 3:19

1 Scripture

2 Soak It In

3 Search Meanings

4 Saying To Me

5 Set Your Mind

6 Share

7 Say It In a Prayer

Forgiven and Healed

Date:

Romans 8:1

1 Scripture

2 Soak It In

3 Search Meanings

4 Saying To Me

5 Set Your Mind

6 Share

7 Say It In a Prayer

Forgiven and Healed

Date:

2 Corinthians 5:17

1 Scripture

2 Soak It In

3 Search Meanings

4 Saying To Me

5 Set Your Mind

6 Share

7 Say It In a Prayer

Forgiven and Healed

Date:

Ephesians 1:7

1 Scripture

2 Soak It In

3 Search Meanings

4 Saying To Me

5 Set Your Mind

6 Share

7 Say It In a Prayer

Forgiven and Healed

Date:

Ephesians 4:32

1 Scripture

2 Soak It In

3 Search Meanings

4 Saying To Me

5 Set Your Mind

6 Share

7 Say It In a Prayer

Forgiven and Healed

Date:

Colossians 1:13-14

1 Scripture

2 Soak It In

3 Search Meanings

4 Saying To Me

5 Set Your Mind

6 Share

7 Say It In a Prayer

Forgiven and Healed

Date:

Colossians 3:13

1 Scripture

2 Soak It In

3 Search Meanings

4 Saying To Me

5 Set Your Mind

6 Share

7 Say It In a Prayer

Forgiven and Healed

Date:

I John 1:9

1 Scripture

2 Soak It In

3 Search Meanings

4 Saying To Me

5 Set Your Mind

6 Share

7 Say It In a Prayer

Beautifully and Wonderfully Made

Beautifully and Wonderfully Made

Date: ____________________

Genesis 1:27

1 Scripture

2 Soak It In

3 Search Meanings

4 Saying To Me

5 Set Your Mind

6 Share

7 Say It In a Prayer

Beautifully and Wonderfully Made

Date:

Psalm 139:14

1 Scripture

2 Soak It In

3 Search Meanings

4 Saying To Me

5 Set Your Mind

6 Share

7 Say It In a Prayer

Beautifully and Wonderfully Made

Date:

Ephesians 4:24

1 Scripture

2 Soak It In

3 Search Meanings

4 Saying To Me

5 Set Your Mind

6 Share

7 Say It In a Prayer

YOU HAVE A PURPOSE

You Have a Purpose

Date:

Job 42:2

1 Scripture

2 Soak It In

3 Search Meanings

4 Saying To Me

5 Set Your Mind

6 Share

7 Say It In a Prayer

You Have a Purpose

Date:

Psalm 57:2

1 Scripture

2 Soak It In

3 Search Meanings

4 Saying To Me

5 Set Your Mind

6 Share

7 Say It In a Prayer

You Have a Purpose

Date:

Psalm 138:8

1 Scripture

2 Soak It In

3 Search Meanings

4 Saying To Me

5 Set Your Mind

6 Share

7 Say It In a Prayer

You Have a Purpose

Date: ______________________

Proverbs 19:21

1 Scripture

2 Soak It In

3 Search Meanings

4 Saying To Me

5 Set Your Mind

6 Share

7 Say It In a Prayer

You Have a Purpose

Date:

Jeremiah 29:11

1 Scripture

2 Soak It In

3 Search Meanings

4 Saying To Me

5 Set Your Mind

6 Share

7 Say It In a Prayer

You Have a Purpose

Date:

Romans 8:28

1 Scripture

2 Soak It In

3 Search Meanings

4 Saying To Me

5 Set Your Mind

6 Share

7 Say It In a Prayer

You Have a Purpose

Date:

Ephesians 2:10

1 Scripture

2 Soak It In

3 Search Meanings

4 Saying To Me

5 Set Your Mind

6 Share

7 Say It In a Prayer

TRUST IN THE LORD

Trust in the Lord

Date: ______________________

Psalm 9:10

1 Scripture

2 Soak It In

3 Search Meanings

4 Saying To Me

5 Set Your Mind

6 Share

7 Say It In a Prayer

Trust in the Lord

Date:

Psalm 56:3

1 Scripture

2 Soak It In

3 Search Meanings

4 Saying To Me

5 Set Your Mind

6 Share

7 Say It In a Prayer

Trust in the Lord

Date: ______________________

Proverbs 3:5-6

1 Scripture

2 Soak It In

3 Search Meanings

4 Saying To Me

5 Set Your Mind

6 Share

7 Say It In a Prayer

Trust in the Lord

Date:

Isaiah 12:2

1 Scripture

2 Soak It In

3 Search Meanings

4 Saying To Me

5 Set Your Mind

6 Share

7 Say It In a Prayer

Trust in the Lord

Date:

Isaiah 26:4

1 Scripture

2 Soak It In

3 Search Meanings

4 Saying To Me

5 Set Your Mind

6 Share

7 Say It In a Prayer

Trust in the Lord

Date:

Jeremiah 17:7

1 Scripture

2 Soak It In

3 Search Meanings

4 Saying To Me

5 Set Your Mind

6 Share

7 Say It In a Prayer

Made in the USA
Monee, IL
26 October 2020

46137266R00125